The Amazing Creatures of Bongo Bongo

Written and Illustrated

by

Armando G. Almaguer

Dedicated to my grandsons Everett and Sullivan,
who I know will be searching for these creatures in their
vivid imagination.

There is a mysterious, forgotten island on the other side of the world. It is called Bongo Bongo.

Is this island far away? Yes, it is far, far, far away. So far away that only the wind that blows over it knows where it is.

Although the island is tiny, it has many different habitats.

It has yellow sandy beaches.

It has hot tropical jungles. It has green grassy plains.

It also has hills and mountains.

And it has the most beautiful sunsets in the world.

When the sun sets, do you think the sun goes to sleep?

Or does it go and shine on the other side of the world?

This island is home to many interesting and amazing creatures that are unknown to the rest of world.
There are small furry animals that do crazy things.

There are out-of-this-world reptiles.
There are strange colorful birds.
And there are incredible insects seen nowhere else.

One thing about the creatures on Bongo Bongo is that they all have very long names.
So, if you want, feel free to give them a short nickname easier for you to say and remember.

I will start you off with a short nickname that I kind of like for each of the creatures.
Then, you can take it from there and give them your own names!

The beautiful golden sand beaches are the perfect home for the Bongo Bongo green-polka-dotted pop out turtle.
Now that's a really long name!

Its yellow shell is beautifully decorated with green polka dots.
Unlike most turtles, this one can pop out of any of the holes in its shell.

Sometimes it will pop its head out of the front of the shell.
Sometimes it will pop out of the sides where the legs normally come out.
And, sometimes, it will even pop its head out of the back of the shell where the tail normally goes!

Let's just call it Popi the pop out turtle.

Popi loves to eat the delicious blue flowers that grow on the water close to the beach.

One incredible insect is the Bongo Bongo purple circle centipede.

It lives in the green jungles of Bongo Bongo.

Because its head and its tail are connected to give it the shape of a circle, it moves in circles!

Can you imagine having to look for food while moving in circles?

Sometimes it moves clockwise.

(Like the clock hands move to the right.)

And, sometimes, it moves counterclockwise.

(Unlike the clock, this time it moves to the left.)

We can call it Charley the circle centipede.

Charley often gets confused when it's going in circles.

So, its brother will tell it "Go left Charley!" or "Go right Charley!"

Sometimes, it helps to have a brother!

Do you have a brother?

The wide-open grassy plains of Bongo Bongo are home to the Bongo Bongo two-tailed, blue-striped zebra.

We can call the two zebras in the picture Zeb and Zena.

Zeb and Zena love running wild and free across the plains as fast as they can.

They have nothing to fear.

You see, luckily for the Zeb and Zena, and the rest of the herd,

there are no lions or cheetahs on Bongo Bongo.

Now, you might think it strange that these zebras have a double tail.
But there is a sensible explanation.
You see, a long, long time ago, the Bongo Bongo zebra had a single tail.

That's right, one tail like all other zebras in the world.
And, like all zebras, it would use its tail to shoo away the annoying flies from its backside.

It would flick its tail to shoo away the fly from its LEFT side.
But the fly would just fly over to its RIGHT side!

Then, the zebra would flick its tail on its RIGHT side.

And the fly would fly back to its LEFT side!

How frustrating that had to be!

Finally, the Bongo Bongo zebra got so tired of missing the flies, that it developed a double tail.
Yes! A tail that splits at the end to have two separate tips!
Now, with its double tail, it can shoo the flies away from BOTH sides at the same time!
The flies never saw it coming.

Nature is amazing!

Bongo Bongo is also home to the giant Bongo Bongo blue-nose grasshopper.

It is the only grasshopper in the world that has a blue nose.

We can call it Bella the blue nose hopper.

Bella has an amazing bright blue nose that glows in the dark!

Can you imagine!

Other than the big blue nose and its very large size, there is nothing else that is special about Bella.

It just spends its day hopping in the green grass looking for food.

No one knows why the giant Bongo Bongo grasshopper has such a big, blue nose.

I guess no one ever bothered to ask it!

There are certain birds in the world that cannot fly.

Like the ostrich and the emu that we are familiar with and have seen at the zoo.

On Bongo Bongo, however, there is a bird that once soared through the skies of Bongo Bongo.

Now, it can no longer fly. This is the Bongo Bongo bobo bird.

Let's just call it Bobo.

There is a good reason why the bobo bird can no longer fly.
You see, the bobo birds love to eat the delicious tree berries that grow everywhere on Bongo Bongo.

Red ones, purple ones, pink ones, blue ones- the bobos eat them all.
They ate so many berries that, eventually, they grew quite heavy.
Much too heavy to fly.

The Bongo Bongo yellow-bellied emerald snake also lives on Bongo Bongo.

If you see the snake, you can see why it has the name it has.

The emerald green skin blends-in with the green grass where the snake lives.

And the yellow belly blends-in with the yellow flowers that grow in the green grass.

We can call it Eddie the emerald snake.

Like most snakes, Eddie loves to eat bird eggs.

It especially loves to eat the scrumptious bobo bird eggs.

But the bobo bird learned very well how to protect its eggs.

It built its nest high up on a hill where the snake could not reach it.

And so, Eddie the emerald snake, had to start eating more veggies.

Do you know what it’s like to give up eating candy for veggies? Poor Eddie.

The nights on Bongo Bongo belong to the Bongo Bongo long-tail balloon bat.
At night, it comes out from the caves where it sleeps away the day to look for food.
The long-tail balloon bat doesn't fly like all other bats in the world.

Its wings are too tiny.
But it can blow itself up like a balloon.
And so it floats in the night sky and rides the air currents looking for food.

Can you imagine catching one of these balloon bats to keep in your room?
I don't think Mom would like that!
Now let's call the bats in the picture below, Babu and Baba.

Babu and Baba ride the warm summer wind of the Bongo Bongo night sky.

Every night they look for their dinner.

Their favorite food is a nice big helping of Bongo Bongo jumbo fireflies.

And every night they go back to their cave with a full tummy!

In the forests of Bongo Bongo, you can find the crazy-looking Bongo Bongo banana beetle.
Since none of the creatures on Bongo Bongo like to eat bananas, the banana beetle protects itself by looking to all the world like a nice, juicy banana which no other creature would want to eat.

We can call it Barney. If you happen to see Barney, please don't try to eat it! It is NOT a banana!

Maybe one day someone will rediscover this mysterious, faraway island called Bongo Bongo.
Maybe you will grow up to be a famous explorer.
Maybe you will be the one able to find this long-lost island paradise.
Maybe one day, you will get to see these incredible and unique creatures yourself!
In the meantime, you can play with Popi, Charley, Zeb, Zena, Bella, Bobo, Eddie, Babu, Baba and Barney as much as you want in your own mind- in your own imagination.

Because, remember, no other place in the world has more amazing creatures than Bongo Bongo!

THE END

Made in the USA
Monee, IL
17 May 2021